BYE BABY BUNTING

and other rhymes

Bye, baby bunting,
Daddy's gone a-hunting,
Gone to get a rabbit skin,
To wrap the baby bunting in.

Old Farmer Giles
Walked seven miles
With his faithful dog, old Rover;
And old Farmer Giles
When he came to the stiles,
Took a run, and jumped clean over.

Little Poll Parrot
    Sat in his garret
Eating toast and tea;
    A little brown mouse
Jumped into the house,
    And stole it all away.

I do not like thee, Doctor Fell,
    The reason why I cannot tell;
But this I know, and know full well,
    I do not like thee, Doctor Fell.

Ipsey Wipsey spider,
Climbing up the spout;
Down came the rain
And washed the spider out;
Out came the sunshine
And dried up all the rain;
Ipsey Wipsey spider,
Climbing up again.

"Who goes there?"
    "A Grenadier."
"What do you want?"
    "A pot of beer?"

Cuckoo, cuckoo, what do you do?
   In April I open my bill;
In May I sing night and day;
   In June I change my tune;
In July I prepare to fly;
   In August away I must.

Terence McDiddler
The three-stringed fiddler
Can charm, if you please,
The fish from the seas.

There was a man and he had nought,
And robbers came to rob him;
He crept up to the chimney pot,
And then they thought they had him.

But he got down on the other side,
And then they could not find him;
He ran fourteen miles in fifteen days,
And never looked behind him.

Dame Trot and her cat
Sat down to chat;
The Dame sat on this side
And puss sat on that.

"Puss," says the Dame,
"Can you catch a rat
Or a mouse in the dark?"
"Purr!" says the cat.

Davy Davy Dumpling,
Boil him in a pot;
Sugar him and butter him;
And eat him while he's hot.

Elsie Marley is grown so fine,
She won't get up to feed the swine,
But lies in bed till eight or nine,
Lazy Elsie Marley.

My mother said, I never should
  Play with the gypsies in the wood.
If I did, then she would say:
  Naughty girl to disobey.

A was an Apple Pie

B Bit it

C Cut it

D Dealt it

E Eat it

F Fought it

G Got it

H Had it

I
Inspected it

J
Jumped for it

K
Kept it

L
Longed for it

M
Mourned for it

N
Nodded at it

O
Opened it

P
Peeped in it

Q
Quartered it

R
Ran for it

S
Stole it

T
Took it

U
Upset it

V
Viewed it

W
Wanted it

XYZ
All wished for a piece in their hand

Hector Protector was dressed all in green;
    Hector Protector was sent to the Queen.
The Queen did not like him,
    No more did the King;
So Hector Protector was sent back again.

Gregory Griggs, Gregory Griggs,
  Had twenty-seven different wigs.
He wore them up, he wore them down,
  To please the people of the town;
He wore them east, he wore them west,
  But he never could tell which he loved the best.

I am his Highness's dog at Kew;
Pray, tell me sir, whose dog are you?

Bat, bat, come under my hat,
And I'll give you a slice of bacon;
And when I bake, I'll give you a cake,
If I am not mistaken.

Molly, my sister, and I fell out,
    And what do you think it was all about?
She loved coffee and I loved tea,
    And that was the reason we could not agree.

Four and twenty tailors
    Went to catch a snail;
The bravest one amongst them
    Dared not touch her tail.
She put out her horns,
    Like a little Kyloe cow.
Run, tailors, run,
    She'll have you all even now!

I had a little hen,
     The prettiest ever seen;
She washed up the dishes,
     And kept the house clean,

She went to the mill
     To fetch me some flour,
And always got home
     In less than an hour.

Little maid, pretty maid, whither goest thou
Down in the meadow to milk my cow.
Shall I go with thee? No, not now;
When I send for thee, then come thou.

She baked me my bread,
She brewed me my ale,

She sat by the fire
And told a fine tale.

A wise old owl sat in an oak,
The more he heard the less he spoke;
The less he spoke the more he heard.
Why aren't we all like that wise old bird?